At the Beach

by Maggie Bridger
illustrated by Meredith Johnson

Sam

Jesse

"I am going to the beach,"
Papa said.
"Who wants to come?"

"I do," said Sam.

"I do, too," said Jesse.
"But I have two more pages
to read in my book."

"What book
are you reading?"
Papa asked.

"It's a good book,"
Jesse said.
"It's about sharks."

"Sharks can eat people," Sam said.

"The book didn't say that," Jesse said.

"Are there sharks at our
little beach, Papa?"
Jesse asked.

"There are small sharks,"
Papa said.

"They are small,
but they have sharp teeth,"
Sam told Jesse.

AB

At the little beach,
Papa read his book.
Sam jumped in the waves.

Jesse didn't want to go
in the water.
He didn't want a shark
to eat him up.

But it was very hot.
Jesse looked at Sam.
Sam was having fun.

Jesse couldn't see
any sharks, so he went
in the water, too.
He jumped in the waves.

"Did you see any sharks,
Sam?" Jesse asked.
Sam didn't say anything.

Jesse looked for Sam,
but he couldn't see him.
Papa was on the beach,
but where was Sam?
Maybe a shark got him!

Just then, something grabbed
Jesse's toe!
Jesse jumped.
Was it a shark?

No, it was Sam!
"No shark will get you
here!" Sam said.
"But **I** can get you!"

"I can get **you**, too,"
Jesse said.
And Jesse and Sam
played shark
for the rest of the day.